Introduction

Welcome to *My Spelling Workbook*. This book has lots of different activities to help you improve your spelling. Here are some tips to show you the best way to use ~~~ ~ook.

- **Learning Words**

  Each list of words in the book has five test columns. ~~ correctly in a test, you can tick the column.

  ### Three ticks in a row show that you know how to spell

  If you do not get three ticks in a row, you write 'T' in t~~ ~~~ when you start your next list of words, you add the word to the table 'Difficult Words I Have Found'. You can also add any other difficult words you find.

- **Look, Say, Cover, Write, Check**

  These words are to remind you of the best way to learn to spell.
  You should follow this when you are learning each word.

- **Recording your Scores**

  At the back of the book, you will find a grid for recording your scores for each unit.
  This will help you to keep track of how you are improving with your spelling.

- **How to Become a Better Speller**

  1. *Have a go!*
     Write the word on the piece of paper.
     Does it look right? If it doesn't look right, try writing it another way.

  2. *Look around your classroom*
     There are probably many words around you that you just didn't notice.

  3. *Use a dictionary*
     Try using a dictionary before you ask a teacher.

  4. *Ask the teacher*
     If you have tried the first three, then ask a teacher for help.

Contents

List Words	Test 1	Test 2	Test 3	Test 4	Test 5	T
advantage						
average						
cottage						
courage						
package						
savage						
hesitate						
private						
unfortunate						
operate						
ecology						
frame						
purchase						
advertise						
habit						
inhabit						
level						
gravel						
sketch						
stretch						
display						
expand						

 Look   Say   Cover   Write Check

Difficult Words I Have Found	Test 1	Test 2	Test 3	T

Word Worm

1. (a) Circle each list word you can find in the word worm.

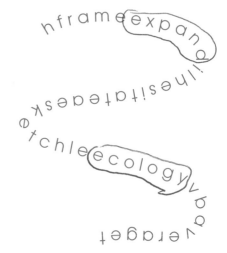

(b) Write the two list words you can make by unjumbling the remaining letters.

_____

_____

Adding Endings

2. Add one of these suffixes to the words below. Check the spelling of your new words with a dictionary.

> ment   ly   ist   ous

(a) unfortunate

   unfortunatly

(b) advertise

   advertisement

(c) private

   privatly

(d) ecology

   ecologyist

(e) courage

   courageous

3. Use list words to solve the crossword.

across

5. To perform an operation
7. Parallel to the horizon
8. Bravery
9. Opposite of shrink
11. Benefit; gain; profit
12. Wild
13. Pause
16. A parcel
17. A rough drawing
18. To make known to the public
19. Opposite of contract

down

1. The border around a picture
2. To show
3. Unlucky
4. Small stones
6. To buy
8. A small house
10. Constant tendency to act in a certain way
11. Ordinary; common; typical
14. To live in (a place)
15. A branch of science dealing with the environment
16. Personal

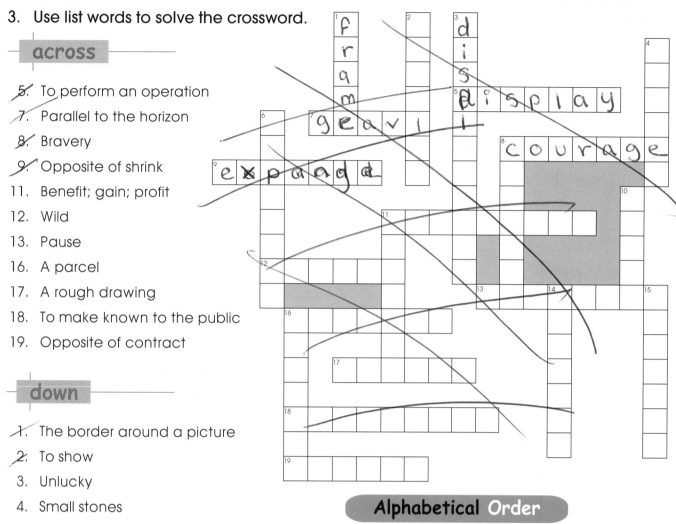

Alphabetical Order

4. Put all the list and revision words starting with the letters 'a', 'b' or 'c' into alphabetical order. (13)

_____

_____

_____

_____

_____

_____

_____

_____

_____

Spelling Challenges

1. Write the list words using look, say, cover, write, check.
2. Write the revision words in alphabetical order.
3. Use a dictionary to write a definition for eight revision words.
4. Sort the list words according to the number of syllables.

UNIT 1

All Mixed Up

List

advantage
average
cottage
courage
package
savage
hesitate
private
unfortunate
operate
ecology
frame
purchase
advertise
habit
inhabit
level
gravel
sketch
stretch
display
expand

5. Unjumble these list words.

(a) aadntvega _advantage_ (b) oucareg _courage_

(c) cpkaega _package_ (d) eedatsivr _advertise_

(e) etasieht _hesitant_ (f) lragve _gravel_

(g) teporae _operate_ (h) avasge _savage_

(i) veearga _average_ (j) atirpve _private_

(k) tahbi _habit_ (l) sidyalp _display_

Antonyms

6. Find a list or revision word with an opposite meaning.

(a) disadvantage _advantage_ (b) life _____

(c) fortunate _unfortunate_ (d) impossible _unimpossible_

(e) contract _____ (f) dusk _____

(g) nephew _neis_ (h) civilised _____

Synonyms

7. Find a list or revision word with a similar meaning.

(a) flat _____ (b) pause _____

(c) buy _____ (d) fabric _____

(e) draw _sketch_ (f) rehearse _____

(g) empty _nothing in_ (h) bravery _courage_

Sentences

8. Write each of these words in a sentence.

(a) courage _The Knight was very courageous in the battle._

(b) courageous _I have great courage._

(c) advantage _I'd nev_

(d) advantageous _____

Revision

climate
aloud
treat
missile
cherry
death
dawn
bare
orphan
verb
practise
tube
aboard
circle
material
niece
sauce
possible
amaze
coffee
tropics
instant

9. Find these list words in the word search.

advantage   ecology

average   frame

cottage   purchase

courage   package

inhabit   savage

hesitate   gravel

private   sketch

unfortunate   stretch

operate   expand

level   habit

h	s	h	p	u	r	c	h	a	s	e	d	a
l	k	e	e	g	a	k	c	a	p	a	l	v
e	e	s	p	e	m	a	r	f	e	n	p	e
t	t	i	r	o	b	l	e	v	a	r	g	r
a	c	t	h	a	b	i	t	d	i	o	n	a
n	h	a	l	e	v	e	l	v	m	c	e	g
u	e	t	e	l	w	e	a	p	o	e	n	e
t	t	e	g	f	r	t	e	t	u	v	e	e
r	a	x	a	n	e	s	t	r	e	t	c	h
o	r	p	r	e	g	a	t	n	a	v	d	a
f	e	a	u	l	g	e	c	o	l	o	g	y
n	p	n	o	e	s	t	i	b	a	h	n	i
u	o	d	c	l	a	f	s	a	v	a	g	e

Small Words

10. Write the list words which contain these small words.

(a) chase _____

(b) bit _____

(c) grave _____

(d) van _____

Memory Master

11. (a) Cover the list words. Write three from memory.

_____   _____   _____

(b) For each word, write a question which has the word as its answer.

(i) _____

(ii) _____

(iii) _____

Incorrect Words

12. Write these words correctly

(a) scetch _____

(b) levle _____

(c) averidge _____

(d) habet _____

(e) curage _____

(f) cottige _____

List Words	Test 1	Test 2	Test 3	Test 4	Test 5	T
rear						
grease						
eagle						
cease						
beast						
breathe						
league						
disappear						
measles						
reasonable						
graze						
organise						
recognise						
realise						
advice						
provide						
strike						
fertile						
crime						
require						
describe						
habitat						

Look	Say	Cover	Write	Check

Difficult Words I Have Found	Test 1	Test 2	Test 3	T

Word Challenge

1. (a) Make at least 10 words from the word in the box. You can rearrange the letters.

   (reasonable)

   _____

   _____

   _____

   _____

   _____

   _____

   (b) Circle the longest word you found.

Anagrams

2. Rearrange the letters in these list and revision words to make a new word. For example,

   same ⟶ seam

   (a) rear _____

   (b) verse _____

   (c) organ _____

   (d) share _____

   (e) beast _____

UNIT 2

3. Use list words to solve the crossword.

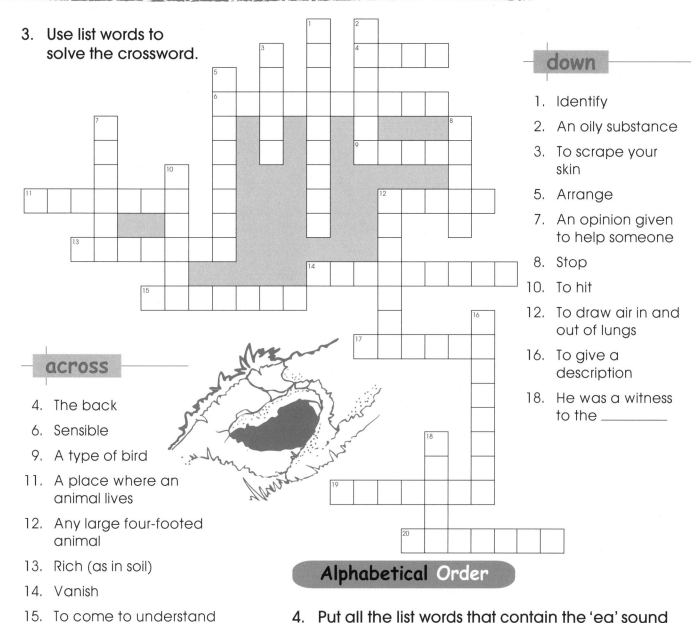

down

1. Identify
2. An oily substance
3. To scrape your skin
5. Arrange
7. An opinion given to help someone
8. Stop
10. To hit
12. To draw air in and out of lungs
16. To give a description
18. He was a witness to the _____

across

4. The back
6. Sensible
9. A type of bird
11. A place where an animal lives
12. Any large four-footed animal
13. Rich (as in soil)
14. Vanish
15. To come to understand
17. A group or association of clubs
19. Need
20. A disease characterised by small red spots on the skin

Alphabetical Order

4. Put all the list words that contain the 'ea' sound into alphabetical order. (11)

_____

_____

_____

_____

_____

Spelling Challenges

1. Write the list words using look, say, cover, write, check.
2. Make word sums from the list words.

   For example, pro + vide = provide

3. Write true or false statements using the revision words.
4. Write the list words in reverse alphabetical order.

UNIT 2

My Meanings

5. Write a definition for each of these words. Use a dictionary to check your answers.

   (a) advice _____

   _____

   (b) measles _____

   _____

   (c) league _____

   _____

   (d) breathe _____

   _____

Antonyms

6. Find a list or revision word with an opposite meaning.

   (a) unreasonable _____ (b) tiny _____

   (c) front _____ (d) commence _____

   (e) proud _____ (f) appear _____

Synonyms

7. Find a list or revision word with a similar meaning.

   (a) referee _____ (b) arrange _____

   (c) vanish _____ (d) retell _____

   (e) distribute _____ (f) understand _____

   (g) environment _____ (h) enormous _____

Sentences

8. Write each of these words in a sentence.

   (a) advise _____

   _____

   (b) advice _____

   _____

List

rear
grease
eagle
cease
beast
breathe
league
disappear
measles
reasonable
graze
organise
recognise
realise
advice
provide
strike
fertile
crime
require
describe
habitat

Revision

chocolate
account
repeat
umpire
berry
breath
awful
share
organ
verse
governor
huge
cupboard
rifle
special
handkerchief
communicate
horrible
ashamed
geese
donkey
cliff

9. Find these list words in the word search.

disappear   graze

rear   organise

grease   realise

eagle   advice

cease   provide

beast   strike

breathe   fertile

league   crime

measles   require

reasonable   describe

b	a	r	u	s	e	e	c	i	v	d	a	c
e	e	e	n	l	s	t	e	o	l	c	h	e
r	e	a	p	l	i	w	h	i	o	r	e	a
e	s	s	i	n	o	t	p	h	i	l	s
q	i	o	d	t	a	e	a	e	a	m	i	e
u	l	n	e	u	g	a	e	l	e	e	t	r
i	a	a	d	o	r	d	r	g	x	n	r	i
r	e	b	l	f	o	s	b	e	r	l	e	e
e	r	l	m	e	a	s	l	e	s	a	f	s
r	u	e	s	e	d	i	v	o	r	p	z	a
a	d	e	s	c	r	i	b	e	a	g	l	e
e	l	s	t	r	i	k	e	n	o	p	e	r
r	a	e	p	p	a	s	i	d	g	r	a	g

Missing Words

10. Use list words to complete the sentences.

(a) I did not _____ my sister when she had the _____.

(b) We _____ a plan and a budget, before we can

_____ the class Christmas party.

(c) 'When we arrive at the zoo, you will

_____ the _____

of the animals,' said our teacher.

Word Hunt

11. Which list or revision words:

(a) are animals? _____

(b) have plurals that end in 'ies'? _____

(c) end in 'le'? _____

_____

Small Words

12. Find small words in these list or revision words.

(a) reasonable _____

(b) disappear _____

(c) habitat _____

(d) handkerchief _____

List Words	Test 1	Test 2	Test 3	Test 4	Test 5	T
envelope						
purpose						
explode						
cartridge						
detail						
curtain						
employ						
destroy						
request						
possess						
poet						
liquid						
oxygen						
knob						
invent						
exhibit						
express						
citizen						
brass						
blossom						
content						
respect						

Look	Say	Cover	Write	Check

Difficult Words I Have Found	Test 1	Test 2	Test 3	T

Word Worm

1. Cross out every second letter. The remaining letters will make three jumbled list words. Write the unjumbled words below.

_____

_____

_____

Word Meanings

2. Write the list word that matches each meaning.

(a) we need it to breathe

_____

(b) a person who writes poetry

_____

(c) letters are sent in this

_____

(d) the flower of a plant

_____

(e) blocks the sunlight

_____

3. Use list words to solve the crossword.

down

1. Neither a gas nor a solid
2. To show a high regard for
3. A window covering
5. A person who lives in a town or city
8. Display
10. The reason for
12. A gas
13. Fact or item
16. Demolish
18. Own

across

4. To make for the first time
5. Happy or satisfied
6. To ask for
7. A person who writes poems
9. A cover for a letter
11. A handle
14. To give work to someone
15. A printer contains a disposable _____
17. To blow up
19. A mixture of copper and zinc
20. To put into words
21. A flower

Alphabetical Order

4. Put all the list and revision words starting with 'c', 'd' or 'e' into alphabetical order. (13)

_____
_____
_____
_____
_____
_____

Spelling Challenges

1. Write the list words using look, say, cover, write, check.
2. Sort the list words according to how many consonants are in each word.
3. Write a meaningful sentence containing each revision word.
4. Write a paragraph using eight of the list words.

All Mixed Up

5. Unjumble the list words.

(a) ixehbti _____ (b) sopsess _____

(c) diuqil _____ (d) nvinet _____

(e) plvneeoe _____ (f) tocnten _____

(g) ossolbm _____ (h) niatruc _____

(i) olpmey _____ (j) absrs _____

(k) pxodlee _____ (l) serpxes _____

Antonyms

6. Find a list or revision word with an opposite meaning.

(a) solid _____ (b) past _____

(c) sweet _____ (d) disrespect _____

(e) create _____ (f) slow _____

(g) dismiss _____ (h) unstable _____

Synonyms

7. Find a list or revision word with a similar meaning.

(a) ask _____ (b) fluid _____

(c) display _____ (d) flower _____

(e) hire _____ (f) below _____

(g) port _____ (h) own _____

Extend Yourself

8. A CD Rom is a laser disc that can store a large amount of text and graphics. Write a definition for each of these other information technology items.

(a) disc _____

(b) mouse _____

(c) scanner _____

(d) modem _____

(e) software _____

(f) hardware _____

List

envelope
purpose
explode
cartridge
detail
curtain
employ
destroy
request
possess
poet
liquid
oxygen
knob
invent
exhibit
express
citizen
brass
blossom
content
respect

Revision

pirate
sour
beneath
excite
hobby
heaven
law
prepare
ordinary
serve
government
future
flight
stable
harbour
CD Rom
sausage
article
swift
skill
machine
bury

9. **Find these list words in the word search.**

purpose   oxygen

explode   knob

detail   invent

curtain   exhibit

employ   express

destroy   citizen

request   brass

possess   blossom

poet   content

liquid   respect

r	o	p	s	t	t	s	e	u	q	e	r	p
i	e	l	o	v	s	s	e	r	p	x	e	o
p	o	s	s	e	s	s	o	p	r	i	l	e
v	e	r	p	i	m	t	b	o	n	k	e	t
o	n	i	c	e	y	x	n	s	s	a	r	b
r	e	n	u	e	c	m	d	e	t	a	i	l
e	g	v	r	y	m	t	o	i	t	l	w	o
s	y	e	t	o	f	p	i	s	u	n	d	a
o	x	n	a	r	e	o	l	b	s	q	o	s
p	o	t	i	t	u	s	e	o	i	o	i	c
r	e	a	n	s	s	m	o	l	y	h	l	l
u	l	o	n	e	z	i	t	i	c	m	x	b
p	l	a	n	d	r	e	d	o	l	p	x	e

Two Meanings

10. The list word **content** has more than one meaning. Write a sentence to show the difference.

_____

_____

_____

Missing Letters

11. Complete these list or revision words.

(a)   __ x __ g __ n   (b) c o n __ __ __ t   (c) __ __ a s __

(d)   __ n o b   (e) e x __ __ __ i t   (f) p __ __ t

(g)   __ __ v __ __ __ m e n t (h) e __ __ e l __ __ e (i) h __ __ b __ __ r

(j)   r __ __ u e __ __   (k) c __ __ t r __ __ __ e (l) s __ __ s a __ e

Memory Master

12. (a) Cover the list words. Write three from memory.

_____   _____   _____

(b) For each word, write a question that has the word as its answer.

(i) _____

(ii) _____

(iii) _____

UNIT 4

List Words	Test 1	Test 2	Test 3	Test 4	Test 5	T
haul						
launch						
laundry						
exhaust						
examine						
excellent						
depart						
argument						
parliament						
popular						
particular						
complete						
improve						
vanish						
false						
discuss						
deliver						
control						
continent						
command						
accept						
goodness						

 Look   Say   Cover   Write   Check

Difficult Words I Have Found	Test 1	Test 2	Test 3	T

Word Challenge

1. (a) Make at least 10 words from the word in the box. You can rearrange the letters.

   (parliament)

   _____

   _____

   _____

   _____

   _____

   _____

   _____

   _____

   _____

   _____

   (b) Circle the longest word you found.

Small Words

2. Write the list words which contain these small words.

   (a) man _____

   (b) good _____

   (c) live _____

   (d) prove _____

   (e) part _____

   (f) mine _____

   (g) van _____

3. Use list words to solve the crossword.

across

4. To have power over
5. Opposite of true
7. To drag or pull
11. Talk about
12. A place where clothes are washed
14. Single, or one rather than all
15. To tire out
17. A disagreement
19. Superior; remarkably good
20. A large mass of land

down

1. To agree with
2. _____ gracious me!
3. Disappear
6. To lead or be in charge of
8. A type of boat
9. Finish
10. To get better
11. To hand over to another person
13. The group of people who make the laws of a country
15. To look at carefully
16. Well liked
18. Leave

Spelling Challenges

1. Write the list words using look, say, cover, write, check.
2. Sort the words according to the number of syllables.
3. Write the revision words in reverse alphabetical order.
4. Write a paragraph containing 10 list words.

Alphabetical Order

4. Put all the list and revision words which have more than two syllables into alphabetical order. (15)

_____

_____

_____

_____

_____

_____

_____

_____

Missing Words

5. Use list words to complete the sentences.

(a) We had to _____ a speech to the class before we

could _____ the assignment.

(b) My socks always seem to _____ when my Mum does

the _____.

(c) We are to _____ for the African _____ on
Thursday.

(d) Using that _____ pen appeared to _____
my handwriting.

(e) The politician had an _____ in _____ this
afternoon.

Antonyms

6. Find a list or revision word with an opposite meaning.

(a) decline _____ (b) appear _____

(c) misunderstood _____ (d) true _____

(e) incomplete _____ (f) combine _____

(g) arrive _____ (h) unpopular _____

Synonyms

7. Find a list or revision word with a similar meaning.

(a) garbage _____ (b) order _____

(c) finish _____ (d) test _____

(e) disappear _____ (f) leave _____

Homonyms

8. Circle the correct word.

(a) The boy decided he would (accept/except) the invitation to his
friend's party.

(b) Everyone (accept/except) John had to visit the dentist for a
check-up.

(c) The captain of the football team was asked to (accept/except)
the trophy for the most improved player.

(d) Place all the ingredients in the pan (accept/except) for the peas.

List

haul
launch
laundry
exhaust
examine
excellent
depart
argument
parliament
popular
particular
complete
improve
vanish
false
discuss
deliver
control
continent
command
accept
goodness

Revision

separate
surround
seam
polite
navy
meant
synthetic
flow
sword
environment
understood
puncture
virtual
valuable
neighbour
centre
question
swarm
swept
sandwich
rubbish
facsimile

9. Find these list words in the word search.

haul	launch
laundry	exhaust
examine	excellent
depart	argument
popular	deliver
complete	control
improve	continent
vanish	command
false	accept
discuss	goodness

y	r	d	n	u	a	l	i	n	e	c	o	g
s	t	r	o	c	r	a	l	u	p	o	p	o
u	s	d	i	s	c	u	s	s	i	m	i	o
l	u	u	v	a	n	i	s	h	s	m	a	d
t	a	e	l	f	t	p	e	c	c	a	e	n
n	h	y	l	a	u	n	c	h	e	n	t	e
e	x	c	e	l	l	e	n	t	v	d	e	s
n	e	l	x	s	t	n	t	r	o	v	l	s
i	m	a	d	e	p	a	r	t	r	l	p	i
t	o	l	o	r	t	n	o	c	p	u	m	p
n	d	e	l	i	v	e	r	i	m	a	o	e
o	e	n	i	m	a	x	e	m	i	h	c	h
c	o	n	t	r	t	n	e	m	u	g	r	a

Memory Master

10. (a) Cover the list words. Write three from memory.

_____   _____   _____

(b) Write an interesting sentence containing each word.

(i) _____

(ii) _____

(iii) _____

Adding Endings

11. Add 'ing' to the words below. Use a dictionary to check your answers.

(a) examine _____   (b) control _____

(c) deliver _____   (d) complete _____

(e) separate _____   (f) vanish _____

(g) surround _____   (h) launch _____

Incorrect Words

12. Write these words correctly.

(a) laundery _____   (b) parlament _____

(c) excelent _____   (d) neighbor _____

(e) seperate _____   (f) sanwhich _____

(g) enviroment _____ (h) ment _____

UNIT 5

List Words	Test 1	Test 2	Test 3	Test 4	Test 5	T
urgent						
murder						
further						
furnish						
disturb						
burglar						
pursuit						
horrify						
satisfy						
occupy						
terrify						
terrific						
steer						
pioneer						
engineer						
squeeze						
degree						
success						
stationery						
agent						
human						
nylon						

Look	Say	Cover	Write	Check

Difficult Words I Have Found	Test 1	Test 2	Test 3	T

Small Words

1. Write the list words which contain these small words.

   (a) an _____

   (b) age _____

   (c) engine _____

   (d) urge _____

   (e) sat _____

   (f) suit _____

   (g) station _____

Past / Present

2. Complete the table.

(a)	squeeze	squeezed
(b)	disturb	
(c)		horrified
(d)	satisfy	
(e)	furnish	
(f)		occupied
(g)	terrify	
(h)		steered

3. Use list words to solve the crossword.

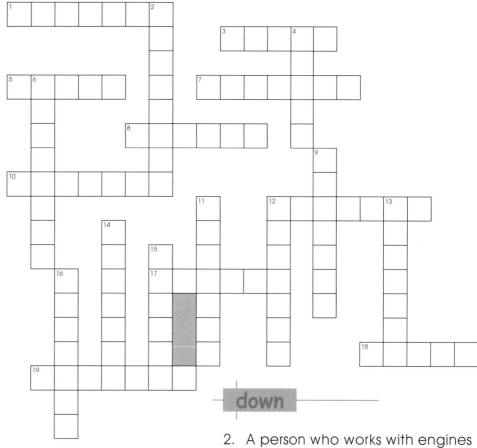

across

1. To push together
3. A man, woman or child
5. To control the direction of a car
7. Opposite of failure
8. A rank or grade
10. An explorer
12. To put furniture into a room or a house
17. Something that requires immediate action
18. A synthetic material used to make stockings
19. Bother

down

2. A person who works with engines or machines
4. A person who acts for another person
6. Excellent
9. To frighten greatly
11. Someone who breaks into a house to steal
12. To advance or promote
13. To fulfil the needs of a person
14. The chase
15. To kill a person on purpose
16. To fill with horror

Alphabetical Order

4. Put all the list and revision words ending in 'y' or 't' into alphabetical order. (12)

_____

_____

_____

_____

_____

_____

Spelling Challenges

1. Write the list words using look, say, cover, write, check.
2. Jumble each of the list words. Give to a friend to unjumble.
3. Write five silly sentences using all the revision words.
4. Use a dictionary to write a definition for eight list words.

All Mixed Up

5. Unjumble the list words.

(a) retrific _____

(b) fsitsay _____

(c) eerged _____

(d) zeeuqse _____

(e) eugrnt _____

(f) rutsidb _____

(g) amuhn _____

(h) negat _____

(i) dumrer _____

(j) tufrher _____

(k) sfiunrh _____

(l) lonny _____

Antonyms

6. Find a list or revision word with an opposite meaning.

(a) uncomfortable _____

(b) friend _____

(c) closer _____

(d) dishonour _____

(e) inhuman _____

(f) failure _____

Synonyms

7. Find a list or revision word with a similar meaning.

(a) guide _____

(b) disrupt _____

(c) fantastic _____

(d) combine _____

(e) push _____

(f) examine _____

(g) thief _____

(h) fulfil _____

Sentences

8. Write each of these words in a sentence.

(a) human _____

_____

(b) humanity _____

_____

(c) success _____

_____

(d) pursuit _____

_____

List

urgent
murder
further
furnish
disturb
burglar
pursuit
horrify
satisfy
occupy
terrify
terrific
steer
pioneer
engineer
squeeze
degree
success
stationery
agent
human
nylon

Revision

celebrate
bound
spear
unite
enemy
feather
prevent
growth
afford
perform
crew
measure
lightning
comfortable
honour
tongue
composition
wharf
daily
inspect
carpenter
shove

9. Find these list words in the word search.

f	u	r	t	h	e	r	r	e	d	r	u	m
c	i	f	e	e	c	y	f	i	r	r	e	t
i	c	e	r	n	s	s	s	e	c	c	u	s
r	o	g	h	a	b	t	s	f	i	s	p	s
x	e	n	t	m	u	r	e	l	o	i	r	t
d	i	s	t	u	r	b	c	e	o	l	e	r
f	y	a	e	h	g	o	c	n	r	r	t	o
u	f	t	z	u	l	i	e	r	r	i	s	t
r	i	i	e	n	a	e	s	i	u	o	n	n
n	r	s	e	o	r	i	f	s	i	e	o	e
i	r	f	u	l	e	i	r	o	g	o	o	g
s	o	y	q	y	c	u	p	a	o	l	l	r
h	h	o	s	n	p	o	c	c	u	p	y	u

urgent	terrific
murder	steer
further	pioneer
furnish	squeeze
disturb	degree
burglar	horrify
pursuit	success
satisfy	agent
occupy	human
terrify	nylon

Two Meanings

10. The list word 'degree' has more than one meaning. Write two sentences to show the difference.

(a) _____

_____

(b) _____

_____

Adding Endings

11. Complete the table.

occupy	occupies	occupied	occupying
terrify			
satisfy			
horrify			
multiply			

My Meanings

12. Write a definition for each of these words. Use a dictionary to check your answers.

(a) urgent _____

(b) terrify _____

(c) pioneer _____

UNIT 6

List Words	Test 1	Test 2	Test 3	Test 4	Test 5	T
interactive						
rapid						
exact						
assembly						
majority						
quantity						
utility						
duty						
interface						
refinery						
steady						
jealous						
weapon						
blast						
tarmac						
attempt						
hawk						
coach						
index						
justice						
natural						
optical						

Look	Say	Cover	Write	Check

Difficult Words I Have Found	Test 1	Test 2	Test 3	T

Word Meanings

1. Write the list word that matches each meaning.

   (a) amount or measure

   _____

   (b) used in fighting

   _____

   (c) to do with seeing

   _____

   (d) the right thing to do

   _____

   (e) wanting what others have

   _____

More Than One

2. Complete this table of plurals.

(a)		hawks
(b)	weapon	
(c)	coach	
(d)		utilities
(e)	duty	
(f)	assembly	
(g)	majority	
(h)	refinery	

3. Use list words to solve the crossword.

across

3. Coming from nature
4. Explosion
5. A bird of prey
8. Even or regular
10. Found at the back of some books
11. Most
14. A public service like the water supply
17. Envious
18. Fast
19. Precise
21. An instrument used for fighting

down

1. A type of bus
2. Fairness or rightly deserved
6. Try
7. Part of an airfield surface
9. A moral obligation
12. A place where something is refined
13. Amount
15. Computer software which responds to the actions of the user
16. Gathering

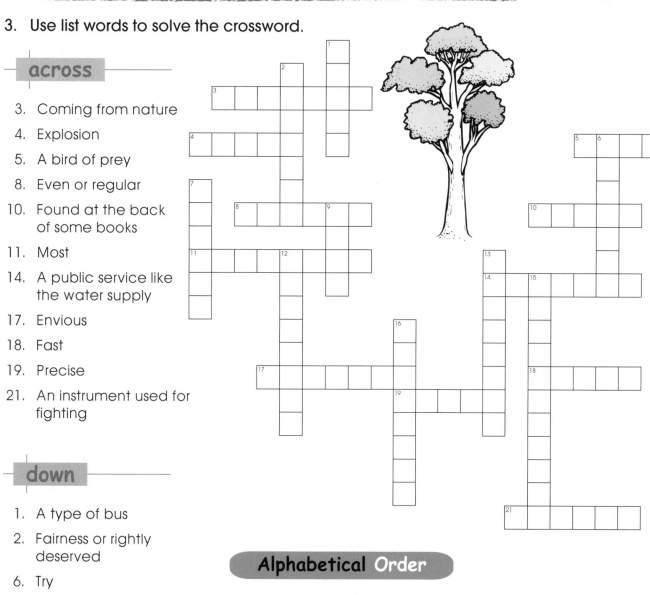

Alphabetical Order

4. Put all the list and revision words which have more than two syllables into alphabetical order. (12)

_____

_____

_____

_____

_____

_____

Spelling Challenges

1. Write the list words using look, say, cover, write, check.
2. Sort the list words according to your own rule. Can a friend guess the rule?
3. Write the revision words in alphabetical order.
4. Sort the list words according to the number of syllables.

UNIT 6

List

interactive
rapid
exact
assembly
majority
quantity
utility
duty
interface
refinery
steady
jealous
weapon
blast
tarmac
attempt
hawk
coach
index
justice
natural
optical

Missing Words

5. Use list words to complete the sentences.

(a) The _____ of the pupils at the

_____ were wearing school uniform.

(b) She felt it was her _____ to set the

_____ free.

(c) The incredible noise had come from the

_____ of the soldier's

_____.

Antonyms

6. Find a list or revision word with an opposite meaning.

(a) inexact _____ (b) slow _____

(c) known _____ (d) synthetic_____

(e) shaky _____ (f) minority _____

(g) injustice _____ (h) disappear _____

Synonyms

7. Find a list or revision word similar in meaning.

(a) amount _____ (b) envious _____

(c) faultless _____ (d) quick _____

(e) try _____ (f) explosion _____

(g) lilac _____ (h) average _____

Revision

bandage
boundary
alive
appear
wealth
problem
unknown
record
perfect
screw
furniture
prove
bundle
splash
favour
truly
addition
violet
tailor
fond
standard
shovel

Sentences

8. In the word 'steady' the 'ea' sound says a short 'e'. Find three other
words with this sound and write them in a sentence.

(a) _____

_____

(b) _____

_____

(c) _____

9. Find these list words in the word search.

interactive   weapon

rapid   blast

exact   steady

tarmac   assembly

jealous   attempt

quantity   natural

hawk   utility

optical   coach

duty   index

refinery   justice

q	u	a	n	t	i	t	y	e	v	e	l	y
d	a	n	o	h	x	c	o	c	o	r	l	d
e	u	i	t	e	e	t	p	i	m	p	r	a
v	n	t	d	i	s	y	t	t	t	a	x	e
i	i	n	y	a	r	r	i	s	c	t	n	t
t	i	o	l	o	a	e	c	u	a	t	o	s
c	y	b	o	o	p	n	a	j	x	e	p	c
a	t	o	r	a	i	i	l	l	e	m	a	o
r	i	l	t	m	d	f	a	h	a	p	e	a
e	l	y	l	b	m	e	s	s	a	t	w	c
t	i	n	a	t	u	r	a	l	k	w	a	h
n	t	t	a	r	m	a	c	n	e	l	k	s
i	u	m	p	e	r	s	u	o	l	a	e	j

Word Worm

10. (a) Circle each list word you can find in the word worm.

exactablastutilityaindexrweaponrapidmccoachthawk

(b) Write the list word you can make by unjumbling the remaining letters.

_____

Memory Master

11. (a) Cover the list words. Write three from memory.

_____ _____ _____

(b) For each word, write a question that has the word as its answer.

(i) _____

(ii) _____

(iii) _____

Small Words

12. Find small words in these list or revision words.

(a) interactive _____

(b) refinery _____

(c) advantage _____

List Words	Test 1	Test 2	Test 3	Test 4	Test 5	T
coarse						
hoarse						
kerosene						
extreme						
blouse						
mount						
doubt						
foul						
council						
bounce						
announce						
incident						
chemist						
criminal						
frequent						
folk						
horizon						
probable						
remarkable						
constable						
suitable						
height						

 Look   **Say**   **Cover**   **Write**   **Check**

Difficult Words I Have Found	Test 1	Test 2	Test 3	T

Word Challenge

1. (a) Make at least 10 words from the word in the box. You can rearrange the letters.

   > remarkable

   _____

   _____

   _____

   _____

   _____

   _____

   (b) Circle the longest word you found.

Small Words

2. Write the list words that contain these small words.

   (a) table

   _____

   (b) suit

   _____

   (c) dent

   _____

   (d) mist

   _____

   (e) eight

   _____

3. Use list words to solve the crossword.

across

5. A major event
6. Happening often
7. People
10. Rough
11. To bound or rebound
15. A fossil fuel used in lamps
18. Where the sky meets the land
19. Very dirty or smelly
20. Fitting the purpose
21. A piece of clothing worn on the upper body
22. Notably unusual

down

1. The distance from bottom to top
2. A person guilty of a crime
3. Inform
4. A person who makes and sells medicines
8. A harsh voice
9. A governing body of a small area
12. To get up on a horse
13. Likely
14. A rank in the police force
16. Far from ordinary
17. Uncertainty

Alphabetical Order

4. Put all the list words that contain 'oa' or 'ou' into alphabetical order. (9)

_____
_____
_____
_____
_____
_____
_____
_____

Spelling Challenges

1. Write the list words using look, say, cover, write, check.
2. Write true or false statements using eight list words.
3. Sort the revision words according to the number of syllables.
4. Write the revision list words in reverse alphabetical order.

All Mixed Up

5. Unjumble the list words.

(a) suoble _____
(b) rtexmee _____
(c) imircanl _____
(d) oubnec _____
(e) tnuom _____
(f) tbuod _____
(g) onnaunec _____
(h) baborpel _____
(i) basnoctel _____
(j) oekresen _____
(k) klof _____
(l) merlbakrae _____

Antonyms

6. Find a list or revision word with an opposite meaning.

(a) success _____
(b) dismount _____
(c) smooth _____
(d) irregular _____
(e) unsuitable _____
(f) niece _____

Synonyms

7. Find a list or revision word with a similar meaning.

(a) last _____
(b) often _____
(c) rough _____
(d) people _____
(e) constant _____
(f) aid _____
(g) fantastic _____
(h) committee _____

Extend Yourself

8. Some prefixes can be used to make a word opposite in meaning. Two of these are 'dis' and 'un'. Using your dictionary, list four examples where these prefixes change the meaning of a word to its opposite. For example, appear — disappear.

dis	un

List

coarse
hoarse
kerosene
extreme
blouse
mount
doubt
foul
council
bounce
announce
incident
chemist
criminal
frequent
folk
horizon
probable
remarkable
constable
suitable
height

Revision

luggage
lounge
advise
holy
palace
attack
shadow
support
merchant
nephew
failure
remove
ankle
shear
margarine
pilot
attention
violin
tadpole
final
regular
model

9. Find these list words in the word search.

coarse   announce

hoarse   incident

kerosene   chemist

extreme   criminal

blouse   frequent

mount   folk

doubt   horizon

foul   probable

suitable   bounce

council

p	e	t	r	i	e	n	e	s	o	r	e	k
r	l	o	c	r	i	m	i	n	a	l	l	i
o	t	i	n	c	i	d	e	n	t	a	l	p
b	l	e	v	e	e	l	b	a	t	i	u	s
a	t	s	i	m	e	h	c	o	u	l	e	t
b	o	r	t	h	g	e	i	h	i	c	c	a
l	m	a	n	e	d	c	o	c	l	i	n	o
e	o	o	e	o	e	n	n	u	m	u	u	f
s	u	c	u	n	d	u	e	s	r	a	o	h
u	n	b	q	u	o	o	n	t	a	l	n	f
o	t	q	e	c	o	b	o	a	k	e	n	u
l	h	o	r	i	z	o	n	g	h	i	a	l
b	l	u	f	i	d	e	m	e	r	t	x	e

My Meanings

10. Write a definition for each of these words. Use a dictionary to check your answers.

(a) probable _____

_____

(b) criminal _____

_____

(c) coarse _____

_____

(d) constable _____

_____

(e) remarkable _____

_____

Adding Endings

11. Add as many of these suffixes as possible to these list words.

(ly   ness   ing   er   ed   ful)

(a) coarse   coarsely   coarseness

(b) announce _____

(c) doubt _____

(d) hoarse _____

(e) frequent _____

List Words	Test 1	Test 2	Test 3	Test 4	Test 5	T
fowl						
tower						
servant						
property						
liberty						
clover						
elder						
fever						
minister						
character						
chapter						
processor						
difference						
entertain						
angler						
binary						
mystery						
observe						
prayer						
process						
pretend						
multimedia						

 Look   Say   Cover   Write   Check

Difficult Words I Have Found	Test 1	Test 2	Test 3	T

More Than One

1. Complete this table of plurals.

(a)	elder	
(b)	fowl	
(c)	exercise	
(d)	mystery	
(e)	binary	
(f)	supply	

Word Meanings

2. Write the list word that matches each meaning.

(a) to amuse

_____

(b) an older person

_____

(c) high body temperature

_____

(d) bird kept for its eggs

_____

(e) made up of two parts

_____

(f) a person who fishes

_____

(g) freedom to do, think and speak

_____

3. Use list words to solve the crossword.

across

2. The head of a government department

4. A type of plant

8. A farmyard bird

9. Senior

11. A person paid to do work for another

12. Consisting of two things

14. The qualities and nature of a person

17. A person who catches fish

20. A machine that processes information

21. To look at

22. Involving several types of media

down

1. High body temperature

3. Possessions or belongings

5. Freedom

6. Amuse

7. A tall, narrow construction

10. The amount separating two numbers

13. A section of a book

15. The way something is done

16. A request made in worship

18. Something puzzling

19. Imagine

Alphabetical Order

4. Put all the list words that contain 'er' in alphabetical order. (16)

_____

_____

_____

_____

_____

Spelling Challenges

1. Write the list words using look, say, cover, write, check.

2. Write a meaningful sentence containing each list word.

3. Write the revision words in reverse alphabetical order.

4. Write a paragraph containing 10 list words.

Missing Words

List

fowl
tower
servant
property
liberty
clover
elder
fever
minister
character
chapter
processor
difference
entertain
angler
binary
mystery
observe
prayer
process
pretend
multimedia

5. Use list words to complete the sentences.

(a) There were _____ all over the farmer's _____ because the gate had been left open that morning.

(b) The _____ of the church sat in silent _____ before the service.

(c) The boy went to _____ the cattle grazing on the _____.

(d) After a lengthy _____ of letter writing and appeals, the prisoner regained his _____.

(e) The disappearance of the _____ from the shore was a _____.

Antonyms

6. Find a list or revision word with an opposite meaning.

(a) shout _____ (b) bore _____

(c) similarity _____ (d) younger _____

Synonyms

7. Find a list or revision word with a similar meaning.

(a) look _____ (b) priest _____

(c) fight _____ (d) tired _____

(e) provide _____ (f) now _____

Sentences

8. Add the prefix 'in' to each of these words and write the new word in a sentence.

| difference | frequent | sincere |

(a) _____
_____

(b) _____
_____

(c) _____
_____

Revision

passage
trousers
exercise
immediately
adult
traffic
swallow
transport
mineral
view
amuse
sincere
wrestle
weary
juice
bough
condition
whisper
supply
vessel
sense
object

9. Find these list words in the word search.

fowl	multimedia
tower	entertain
servant	angler
property	binary
liberty	mystery
clover	observe
elder	prayer
fever	process
minister	pretend
chapter	

e	l	i	b	e	r	t	y	l	a	o	f	y
o	l	b	r	o	y	t	r	e	p	o	r	p
b	o	d	y	r	a	n	i	b	w	n	e	r
s	p	r	e	t	e	n	d	l	c	o	k	l
e	n	t	e	r	t	a	i	n	l	r	f	n
r	a	n	g	l	e	r	a	c	o	e	r	r
v	m	v	t	r	n	t	o	l	v	n	e	e
e	r	n	o	f	s	h	n	e	e	o	y	t
c	e	t	w	i	l	h	r	a	r	e	a	p
t	y	r	e	t	s	y	m	m	v	i	r	a
i	s	p	r	o	c	e	s	s	g	r	p	h
m	i	n	i	s	t	e	r	t	o	p	e	c
m	u	l	t	i	m	e	d	i	a	y	m	s

Incorrect Words

10. Write these words correctly.

(a) binery _____

(b) mistery _____

(c) entertane _____

(d) towre _____

(e) procesor _____

(f) differense _____

Memory Master

11. (a) Cover the list words. Write three from memory.

_____   _____   _____

(b) Write an interesting sentence containing each word.

(i) _____

(ii) _____

(iii) _____

Adding Endings

12. Complete the table.

process	processes	processed	processing
entertain			
		pretended	
	towers		
			swallowing
observe			

List Words	Test 1	Test 2	Test 3	Test 4	Test 5	T
nervous						
generous						
marvellous						
tremendous						
visible						
sensible						
scramble						
struggle						
rattle						
puzzle						
badge						
humour						
labour						
neighbourhood						
suggest						
progress						
regret						
reflect						
represent						
select						
widow						
hollow						

Look	Say	Cover	Write	Check

Difficult Words I Have Found	Test 1	Test 2	Test 3	T

Word Worm

1. (a) Circle each list word you can find in the word worm.

vibrattleeepuzzletiwidowlelo bourssregretlc

(b) Write the two list words you can make by unjumbling the remaining letters.

_____

_____

Small Words

2. Write the list words that contain these small words.

(a) low

_____

(b) sent

_____

(c) men

_____

(d) ram

_____

(e) rat

_____

(f) rug

_____

3. Use list words to solve the crossword.

across

1. Portray or depict
4. The ability to see things in a funny way
10. To jumble up
11. A brooch-like ornament
12. To throw back light or heat
13. To move with difficulty
17. Anxious
19. To work hard
21. Able to be seen

down

2. Advise or hint
3. Confuse
5. Choose
6. Empty inside
7. Extraordinarily large or strong
8. Shaken by a baby to make a noise
9. The area in which you live
13. Wise or reasonable
14. A woman whose husband has died
15. Kind and giving
16. Amazing
18. Advance or go forward
20. To feel sorry about something

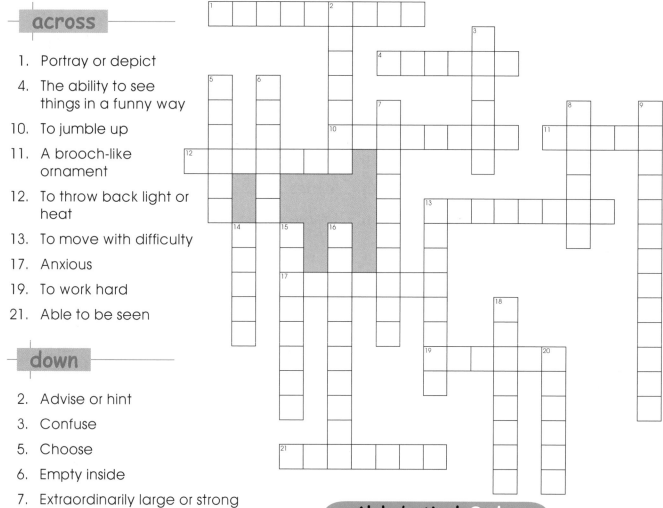

Alphabetical Order

4. Put all the list and revision words starting with 'r', 's' or 't' into alphabetical order. (15)

_____

_____

_____

_____

_____

_____

_____

Spelling Challenges

1. Write the list words using look, say, cover, write, check.
2. Write each of the revision words in a question.
3. Sort the list words according to the number of syllables.
4. Use a dictionary to write a definition for 10 list words.

All Mixed Up

5. Unjumble the list words.

(a) muhuor _____

(b) lgurtsge _____

(c) esererptn _____

(d) olohlw _____

(e) urenvos _____

(f) abdge _____

(g) lttare _____

(h) gerret _____

(i) elbisiv _____

(j) lbisnese _____

(k) egorprss _____

(l) tnemerduos _____

Antonyms

6. Find a list or revision word with an opposite meaning.

(a) tiny _____

(b) solid _____

(c) regress _____

(d) invisible _____

(e) accept _____

(f) exit _____

Synonyms

7. Find a list or revision word with a similar meaning.

(a) choose _____

(b) wander _____

(c) fantastic _____

(d) anxious _____

(e) many _____

(f) logo _____

(g) recommend _____

(h) soft _____

Missing Words

8. Using a word built from one of these words, complete the following sentences.

| scramble | struggle | regret | humour |

(a) The boy had always _____ not helping his friend.

(b) The children _____ up the bank after the puppies.

(c) The teacher did not find the practical joke very _____ .

(d) The kidnapped girl _____ to free herself.

(e) They had to _____ the code to play the game.

(f) The boy was _____ to read the difficult words in the newspaper.

List

nervous
generous
marvellous
tremendous
visible
sensible
scramble
struggle
rattle
puzzle
badge
humour
labour
neighbourhood
suggest
progress
regret
reflect
represent
select
widow
hollow

Revision

brigade
wound
roam
weave
industry
adopt
result
bullet
enormous
several
bathe
refuse
global
gentle
weave
ruin
graphic
direction
youth
cotton
wander
although
entrance

9. Find these list words in the word search.

t	h	n	e	e	l	b	m	a	r	c	s	w
h	u	o	s	s	e	r	g	o	r	p	i	r
i	m	t	c	e	l	e	s	t	a	d	y	o
s	o	e	t	s	a	l	u	n	o	r	e	t
u	u	l	s	s	b	z	s	w	a	t	e	a
o	r	b	e	u	o	z	u	i	s	r	o	b
l	a	i	g	o	u	u	o	n	g	r	a	e
l	t	s	g	r	r	p	v	e	n	d	l	e
e	t	i	u	e	s	t	r	u	g	g	l	e
v	l	v	s	n	t	o	e	e	a	v	m	h
r	e	p	r	e	s	e	n	t	e	o	l	s
a	p	r	c	g	e	t	c	e	l	f	e	r
m	a	c	a	i	e	l	b	i	s	n	e	s

nervous   humour

generous   labour

marvellous   suggest

visible   progress

sensible   regret

scramble   reflect

struggle   represent

rattle   select

puzzle   widow

badge

My Meanings

10. Write a definition for each of these words. Use a dictionary to check your answers.

   (a)   puzzle _____

   (b)   progress _____

   (c)   sensible _____

   (d)   reflect _____

Memory Master

11. (a) Cover the list words. Write three from memory.

   _____   _____   _____

   (b) For each word, write a question that has the word as its answer.

      (i)   _____

      (ii) _____

      (iii) _____

Word Challenge

12. (a) Make at least 10 words from the word in the box. You can rearrange the letters.

   (tremendous)

   _____

   _____

   (b) Circle the longest word you found.

UNIT 10

List Words	Test 1	Test 2	Test 3	Test 4	Test 5	T
cure						
agriculture						
creature						
departure						
manufacture						
moisture						
pasture						
temperature						
pressure						
costume						
perfume						
tune						
audience						
automatic						
event						
eventually						
severe						
design						
jewel						
chorus						
worst						
clerk						

 Look Say Cover Write Check

Difficult Words I Have Found	Test 1	Test 2	Test 3	T

Word Meanings

1. Write the list word that matches each meaning.

   (a) a measure of the degree of heat and cold

   _____

   (b) a cut and polished stone

   _____

   (c) something that operates by itself

   _____

   (d) an occupation

   _____

   (e) the group of people you would find at a concert

   _____

Small Words

2. Write the list words which contain these small words.

   (a) sure _____

   (b) eat _____

   (c) die _____

   (d) or _____

   (e) ever _____

   (f) fume _____

   (g) mat _____

   (h) fact _____

   (i) art _____

3. Use list words to solve the crossword.

down

2. Farming
3. Done without thought
4. Finally
5. A sweet smelling liquid
8. Very harsh or serious
11. A melody
14. A ground covered with grass
16. To put force on or against
18. An office worker

across

1. To make something in large quantities
6. An animal
7. An important happening
9. To preserve by drying or salting
10. Dampness
12. A group of people watching or listening to a performance
13. Moving away or leaving
15. The repeated part of a song
17. How hot or cold something is
19. The shape or form of something
20. A precious stone
21. Something bad to the highest degree
22. A set of clothes

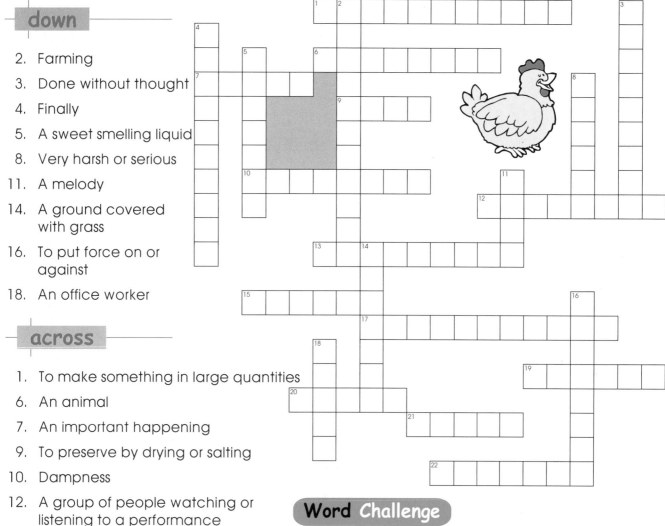

Word Challenge

4. (a) Make at least 10 words from the word in the box. You can rearrange the letters. Circle the longest word you find.

temperature

_____

_____

_____

_____

(b) Circle the longest word you found.

Spelling Challenges

1. Write the list words using look, say, cover, write, check.
2. Sort the list words according to your own rule. Can a friend guess the rule?
3. Write six silly sentences. You must use all of the list words within the sentences.
4. Jumble 10 revision words. Give to a friend to unjumble.

Word Worm

List

5. (a) Circle each list word you can find in the word worm.

msevereventtcurejeweltcmoisture
isnuohcuoerutarepmetsrowaddylautneve

(b) Write the list word you can make by unjumbling the remaining

letters. _____

Antonyms

6. Find a list or revision word with an opposite meaning.

(a) arrival_____ (b) best _____

(c) deny _____ (d) dryness _____

(e) mild _____ (f) double _____

Synonyms

7. Find a list or revision word with a similar meaning.

(a) scent _____ (b) sole _____

(c) student _____ (d) illness _____

(e) parasol _____ (f) double _____

Sentences

8. Write each of these list words in a sentence.

(a) design _____
_____

(b) creature _____
_____

(c) moisture _____
_____

(d) pressure _____
_____

List

cure
agriculture
creature
departure
manufacture
moisture
pasture
temperature
pressure
costume
perfume
tune
audience
automatic
event
eventually
severe
design
jewel
chorus
worst
clerk

Revision

trade
splendid
throat
disease
admit
pupil
length
bomb
uniform
concert
electronic
poison
millennium
single
umbrella
document
examination
business
dye
national
altogether
court

9. Find these list words in the word search.

s	c	a	r	t	c	e	r	u	t	s	a	p
t	r	a	u	d	i	e	n	c	e	l	t	r
t	e	e	m	u	t	s	o	c	u	r	e	o
s	a	v	p	l	a	t	d	e	y	e	r	n
r	t	h	e	l	m	o	n	l	a	c	i	g
o	u	e	o	n	o	u	l	k	h	a	r	i
w	r	m	i	l	t	a	b	o	r	d	i	s
l	e	u	e	r	u	t	r	a	p	e	d	e
e	u	f	r	t	a	u	p	s	t	h	l	d
w	g	r	n	u	s	e	v	e	r	e	t	c
e	t	e	m	p	e	r	a	t	u	r	e	h
j	v	p	l	l	e	r	u	s	s	e	r	p
e	u	r	t	l	e	r	u	t	s	i	o	m

cure   jewel

chorus   worst

clerk   costume

perfume   tune

creature   audience

departure   automatic

moisture   event

pasture   eventually

temperature   severe

pressure   design

Better Words

10. Write a list word that is a synonym for the words in bold print.

(a) Daniel joined in the game **after a period of time**.   _____

(b) The choir sang the **repeated part of the song** five times.   _____

(c) Most of the **people who were watching the play** walked out before the performance had finished.   _____

Alphabetical Order

11. Put the list and revision words starting with 'c' into alphabetical order. (7)

_____

_____

_____

_____

_____

_____

_____

Memory Master

12. (a) Cover the list words. Write three from memory.

_____

_____

_____

(b) For each word, write a question that has the word as its answer.

(i) _____

_____

(ii) _____

_____

(iii) _____

_____

UNIT 11

List Words	Test 1	Test 2	Test 3	Test 4	Test 5	T
ornament						
anchor						
editor						
mirror						
inform						
sensor						
forehead						
import						
export						
memory						
territory						
scissors						
fierce						
shield						
mischief						
achieve						
meanwhile						
theatre						
pigeon						
ache						
spreadsheet						
opposite						

 Look Say Cover Write Check

Difficult Words I Have Found	Test 1	Test 2	Test 3	T

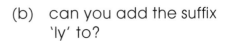

Word Hunt

1. Which list words:

   (a) have a silent 'h'?

   _____

   _____

   (b) can you add the suffix 'ly' to?

   _____

   (c) contain three or more of the same letter?

   _____

   _____

   _____

   (d) are things you may be able to hold in your hand?

   _____

   _____

   _____

   _____

   _____

   (e) are parts of the body?

   _____

   (f) are occupations?

   _____

2. Use list words to solve the crossword.

across

2. A device that detects change
5. A region of land
6. Used for organising data into tables
8. Part of the head
12. To make known
14. A type of bird
15. A decoration
17. A pain
18. Opposite to import
20. An instrument with two blades
21. Accomplish

down

1. The thoughts stored in the mind
3. Contrary or conflicting
4. At the same time
7. A heavy piece of iron used to stop ships and boats from drifting
9. A person who edits books
10. A place for public performances
11. Opposite of export
13. Violent
16. Something that reflects light
19. Naughtiness
20. A piece of armour carried in the hand

Spelling Challenges

1. Write the list words using look, say, cover, write, check.
2. Sort the list words according to the number of syllables.
3. Write a paragraph containing 10 list words.
4. Use a dictionary to write a definition for six list words.

Memory Master

3. (a) Cover the list words. Write three from memory.

_____   _____   _____

(b) For each word, write a question that has the word as its answer.

(i) _____

(ii) _____

(iii) _____

UNIT 11

All Mixed Up

4. Unjumble the list words.

(a) herofdae _____

(b) ssicsros _____

(c) lihwnaeme _____

(d) resson _____

(e) rrimro _____

(f) earonmnt _____

(g) tirretroy _____

(h) ropmit _____

(i) noegip _____

(j) leihsd _____

(k) onachr _____

(l) isoppoet _____

(m) reifce _____

(n) idetor _____

Antonyms

5. Find a list or revision word with an opposite meaning.

(a) fail _____

(b) decrease _____

(c) export _____

(d) usually _____

(e) timid _____

(f) coward _____

(g) fiction _____

(h) same _____

Synonyms

6. Find a list or revision word with a similar meaning.

(a) tell _____

(b) pain _____

(c) trouble _____

(d) antonym _____

(e) protect _____

(f) dishearten _____

More Than One

7. Complete this table of plurals.

(a)	theatre	
(b)		pigeons
(c)	ache	
(d)	territory	
(e)	memory	

8. Find these list words in the word search.

f	i	e	r	c	e	v	r	o	s	n	e	s
r	m	v	n	o	e	g	i	p	m	r	o	e
m	r	o	f	n	i	r	l	s	i	e	p	e
o	t	h	e	a	t	r	e	i	r	v	p	n
d	i	s	i	m	p	o	r	t	r	e	o	d
d	v	r	h	o	r	t	a	f	o	i	s	l
a	v	o	c	o	v	o	r	e	r	h	i	e
e	m	t	s	o	l	e	h	o	r	c	t	i
h	e	i	i	s	h	i	l	c	p	a	e	h
e	m	d	m	c	a	s	r	e	n	x	o	s
r	o	e	a	e	l	i	h	w	n	a	e	m
o	r	n	a	m	e	n	t	l	i	t	u	r
f	y	t	h	e	s	r	o	s	s	i	c	s

ornament   fierce

anchor   shield

editor   mischief

mirror   achieve

inform   meanwhile

forehead   theatre

import   pigeon

export   ache

memory   sensor

scissors   opposite

Extend Yourself

9. 'Meanwhile' and 'forehead' are compound words. Use a dictionary to help you write two more compound words starting with each letter below.

b:

g:

s :

My Meanings

10. Write a definition for each of these words. Use a dictionary to check your answers.

(a) saddle _____

_____

(b) tennis _____

_____

(c) anchor _____

_____

(d) theatre _____

_____

List Words	Test 1	Test 2	Test 3	Test 4	Test 5	T
develop						
accommodation						
statement						
settlement						
instrument						
equipment						
delighted						
drought						
depth						
strength						
method						
freight						
wrist						
due						
pursue						
statue						
oasis						
science						
embarrass						
scone						
social						
siren						

Look   **Say**   **Cover**   **Write**   **Check**

Difficult Words I Have Found	Test 1	Test 2	Test 3	T

Word Worm

1. (a) Circle each list word you can find in the word worm.

methodfdrought wrist hind

developursuedsocialegtsirenre

(b) Write two list words you can make from unjumbling the remaining letters.

_____

_____

Word Challenge

2. (a) Make at least 10 words from the word in the box. You can rearrange the letters. Circle the longest word you find.

(equipment)

_____

_____

_____

_____

_____

_____

_____

(b) Circle the longest word you found.

3. Use list words to solve the crossword.

across

2. Owed

4. To follow or seek

6. The tools or machines needed to do a job

10. A long period of time without rain

11. Create over a period of time

12. Highly pleased

13. Report

14. To make uncomfortable

15. Force or power

16. Living in communities

18. Cargo or load

19. A tool

down

1. A place in the desert where water is found

2. How deep something is

3. A way of doing something

5. A carving of a person in stone

7. A place to stay and live

8. A small cake

9. A systematic study of people and the environment

13. An arrangement or agreement

16. A warning noise

17. Part of the arm

Past / Present

4. Complete the table.

(a)	develop	
(b)		delighted
(c)	pursue	
(d)	embarrass	

Spelling Challenges

1. Write the list words using look, say, cover, write, check.

2. Write true or false statements using 10 revision words.

3. Sort the list words according to the number of consonants in each word.

4. Make word sums for 10 list words. For example, res + cue = rescue

UNIT 12

All Mixed Up

5. Unjumble the list words.

(a) nicsece _____

(b) tgnertsh _____

(c) atstnemet _____

(d) esrpuu _____

(e) erisn _____

(f) murtsinnte _____

(g) otmehd _____

(h) thgodru _____

(i) edu _____

(j) aicosl _____

(k) htped _____

(l) piuqenemt _____

(m) ovedelp _____

(n) etestlemnt _____

Missing Words

6. Using a word built from one of these words, complete the following sentences.

embarrass   develop   strength   statue

(a) Jessie felt very _____ when she had to perform in the concert.

(b) While the film was _____ , he was fixing his camera lens.

(c) There are many beautiful marble _____ in this garden.

(d) 'What do you think will be your _____ and weaknesses on this project?' asked the manager.

Missing Letters

7. Write 'ie' or 'ei' to complete these words.

(a) th____f

(b) bel____ve

(c) rec____pt

(d) ch____f

(e) fr____nd

(f) s____ze

(g) c____ling

(h) f____ld

(i) n____ther

(j) f____rce

(k) rec____ve

(l) h____ght

My Meanings

8. Write a definition of these words. Use a dictionary to check your answers.

(a) siren _____

(b) embarrass _____

(c) delighted _____

List

develop
accommodation
statement
settlement
instrument
equipment
delighted
drought
depth
strength
method
freight
wrist
due
pursue
statue
oasis
science
embarrass
scone
social
siren

Revision

paste
seek
scratch
peace
waist
linen
orchard
surf
decorate
modern
fool
value
frozen
example
scene
halves
population
wreck
worse
passenger
connect
virus

9. **Find these list words in the word search.**

develop   wrist

statement   due

settlement   pursue

equipment   statue

delighted   oasis

drought   science

depth   embarrass

strength   scone

method   social

freight   siren

d	e	t	h	g	i	l	e	d	r	e	u	d
s	m	e	o	r	s	t	a	t	u	e	e	s
d	e	c	a	d	u	t	u	f	e	v	c	c
t	t	n	s	e	u	n	r	e	e	o	l	i
n	h	e	i	m	t	e	n	l	n	o	t	s
e	o	i	s	u	i	m	o	e	t	s	s	s
m	d	c	o	g	u	p	u	r	s	s	i	a
e	d	s	h	l	a	i	c	o	s	e	r	r
l	i	t	d	r	o	u	g	h	t	u	w	r
t	s	i	r	e	n	q	o	p	w	s	r	a
t	g	h	t	g	n	e	r	t	s	r	a	b
e	i	h	t	p	e	d	a	n	b	u	l	m
s	t	a	t	e	m	e	n	t	o	p	l	e

Extend Yourself

10. (a) Some of the list words end in 'ment'. Find five more words that end in 'ment'.

_____ _____ _____

_____ _____

(b) Circle the type of words your 'ment' words are.

nouns   verbs   adverbs   adjectives

Sentences

11. Write each of these list words in a sentence.

(a) oasis _____

_____

(b) drought _____

_____

(c) statement _____

_____

(d) equipment _____

_____

(e) pursue _____

UNIT 13

List Words	Test 1	Test 2	Test 3	Test 4	Test 5	T
elect						
paraplegic						
action						
section						
motion						
plantation						
recreation						
occupation						
invitation						
irrigation						
education						
destination						
conversation						
association						
production						
competition						
affectionate						
nuisance						
instance						
substance						
assistance						
cereal						

Look	Say	Cover	Write	Check

Difficult Words I Have Found	Test 1	Test 2	Test 3	T

Small Words

1. Find small words in these list words.

   (a)   action _____

   (b)   nuisance _____

   (c)   substance _____

   (d)   assistance _____

   _____

   (e)   paraplegic _____

   _____

   (f)   cereal _____

   (g)   destination _____

   _____

Word Meanings

2. Write the list word that matches each meaning.

   (a)   something that bothers you

   _____

   (b)   eaten for breakfast

   _____

   (c)   you might receive one of these by post

   _____

   (d)   to nominate someone

   _____

   (e)   where you arrive at the end of a journey

   _____

   (f)   part of a whole

   _____

3. Use list words to solve the crossword.

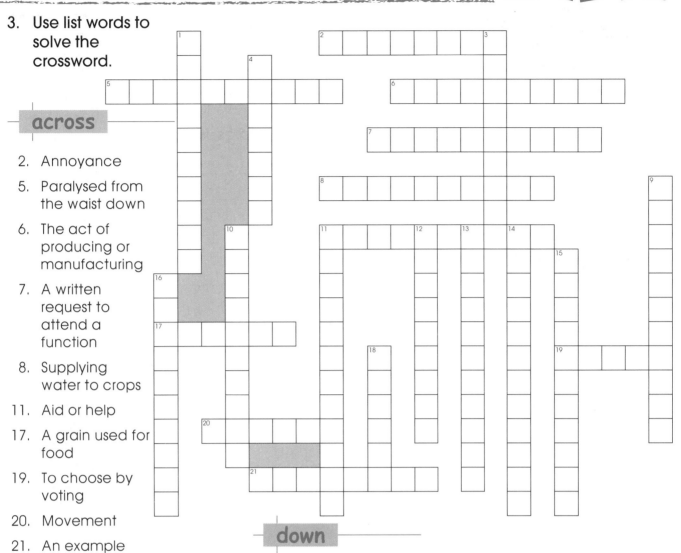

across

2. Annoyance

5. Paralysed from the waist down

6. The act of producing or manufacturing

7. A written request to attend a function

8. Supplying water to crops

11. Aid or help

17. A grain used for food

19. To choose by voting

20. Movement

21. An example

down

1. An estate for growing crops like bananas and cotton

3. The process of gaining knowledge and understanding

4. A part of

9. The place to which you are going

10. Enjoyable activities done in spare time

11. Loving

12. Anything that can be seen or felt

13. A club or society

14. A talk or an exchange of ideas

15. A game or match

16. A person's job or trade

18. A deed

Homonyms

4. Circle the correct word.

(a) I don't like eating (cereal, serial) for breakfast; I prefer toast.

(b) There is a great comedy (cereal, serial) on television tonight.

Spelling Challenges

1. Write the list words using look, say, cover, write, check.

2. Write a nonsense paragraph containing fifteen list words.

3. Write the revision words in reverse alphabetical order.

4. Sort the list words according to the number of vowels in each word.

Memory Master

List

elect
paraplegic
action
section
motion
plantation
recreation
occupation
invitation
irrigation
education
destination
conversation
association
production
competition
affectionate
nuisance
instance
substance
assistance
cereal

5. (a) Cover the list words. Write three from memory.

_____ _____ _____

(b) For each word, write a question that has the word as its answer.

(i) _____

(ii) _____

(iii) _____

Antonyms

6. Find a list or revision word with an opposite meaning.

(a) hindrance _____ (b) unloving _____

(c) disobey _____ (d) southern _____

Synonyms

7. Find a list or revision word with a similar meaning.

(a) movement _____ (b) job _____

(c) part _____ (d) discussion _____

(e) pest _____ (f) help _____

(g) crush _____ (h) forest _____

Sentences

8. Write each of these list words in a sentence.

(a) recreation _____

_____

(b) affectionate _____

_____

(c) destination _____

_____

(d) conversation _____

_____

(e) occupation _____

_____

Revision

mistake
speech
snatch
plastic
obtain
limit
starch
surface
therefore
northern
stoop
rescue
extra
squash
laptop
cardigan
nation
concrete
obey
chalk
judge
region

9. Find these list words in the word search.

competition   irrigation

invitation   recreation

assistance   occupation

association   education

destination   nuisance

production   section

cereal   instance

motion   ˙action

plantation   substance

c	o	m	p	e	t	i	t	i	o	n	o	d
n	o	i	t	a	t	i	v	n	i	t	s	e
l	a	e	r	e	c	n	a	s	i	u	n	s
e	n	o	i	t	a	t	n	a	l	p	o	t
c	m	e	l	l	c	t	i	o	n	o	i	i
n	o	c	c	u	p	a	t	i	o	n	t	n
a	t	n	o	i	t	a	c	u	d	e	a	a
t	i	a	c	t	i	o	n	i	o	t	e	t
s	o	t	n	o	i	t	a	g	i	r	r	i
i	n	s	t	a	n	c	e	t	o	n	c	o
s	t	b	s	e	c	t	i	o	n	t	e	n
s	i	u	n	o	i	t	c	u	d	o	r	p
a	s	s	o	c	i	a	t	i	o	n	d	e

Alphabetical Order

10. Put all the list and revision words starting with 'c' or 's' into alphabetical order. (14)

_____

_____

Adding Endings

11. Write the correct suffix for these words.

ed   al

(a) motion _____

(b) conversation _____

(c) pursue _____

(d) recreation _____

(e) occupation _____

(f) elect _____

Word Worm

12. (a) Circle each list word you can find in the word worm.

(b) Write the list word you can make by unjumbling the remaining letters.

_____

UNIT 14

List Words	Test 1	Test 2	Test 3	Test 4	Test 5	T
curious						
serious						
various						
victory						
fashion						
cushion						
occasion						
provision						
division						
decision						
permission						
seize						
ceiling						
receipt						
route						
tourist						
dare						
rare						
spare						
declare						
pyjamas						
smuggler						

 Look   Say   Cover   Write   Check

Difficult Words I Have Found	Test 1	Test 2	Test 3	T

Anagrams

1. Rearrange the letters in each list or revision word to make a new word. For example,

draw ⟶ ward

(a) spare _____

(b) scent _____

(c) rare _____

(d) dare _____

Word Hunt

2. Which list and revision words:

(a) rhyme with 'pair'?

_____

_____

_____

(b) contain a double consonant?

_____

_____

_____

_____

_____

(c) might describe someone's personality?

_____

_____

(d) are made from fabric?

_____

_____

3. Use list words to solve the crossword.

down

2. Important or significant
4. Course
5. Extra
7. A person who smuggles
8. Something to rest on
10. The 'roof' of a room
11. Worn in bed
13. A judgement
14. To take hold of
15. Opposite to multiplication
16. To win
18. Approval or consent
19. To make known

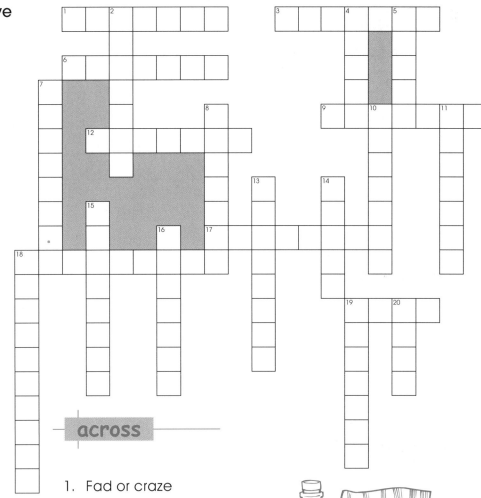

across

1. Fad or craze
3. Traveller on holidays
6. Diverse or mixed
9. A note saying that money has been received
12. Inquisitive
17. A particular time or event
18. A supply of food
19. To challenge or take a risk

Extend Yourself

4. The word 'seize' has many synonyms. Write five words that are synonyms of seize.

_____
_____
_____
_____
_____

Spelling Challenges

1. Write the list words using look, say, cover, write, check.
2. Make words sums for 10 list words. For example,
   diff + i + cult = difficult
3. Sort the list words according to the number of consonants in each word.
4. Write true or false statements using eight list words.

All Mixed Up

5. Unjumble these list words.

(a) rapse _____
(b) noisiced _____

(c) irseosu _____
(d) nosvoprii _____

(e) piecert _____
(f) giiceln _____

(g) uiucros _____
(h) viorasu _____

(i) rrae _____
(j) noihsaf _____

(k) gusmglre _____
(l) amajpys _____

Antonyms

6. Find a list or revision word with an opposite meaning.

(a) release _____
(b) multiplication _____

(c) floor _____
(d) common _____

(e) careful _____
(f) forget _____

Synonyms

7. Find a list or revision word with a similar meaning.

(a) pillow _____
(b) explode _____

(c) traveller _____
(d) trend _____

(e) way _____
(f) perfume _____

Sound Search

8. In the word 'ceiling' the letter 'c' makes an 's' sound. Find four other words where 'c' makes and 's' sound and write them in a sentence.

(a) _____
_____

(b) _____
_____

(c) _____
_____

(d) _____
_____

List

curious
serious
various
victory
fashion
cushion
occasion
provision
division
decision
permission
seize
ceiling
receipt
route
tourist
dare
rare
spare
declare
pyjamas
smuggler

Revision

scale
freedom
hatch
elastic
contain
wedding
harvest
burst
explore
remember
goose
continue
cocoa
shower
scent
careless
international
console
musical
union
cough
million

9. Find these list words in the word search.

curious	ceiling
serious	receipt
various	route
fashion	tourist
cushion	dare
occasion	rare
provision	spare
division	declare
decision	pyjamas
seize	smuggler

o	c	c	a	s	i	o	n	e	z	i	e	s
p	u	g	l	i	n	t	s	i	r	u	o	t
a	r	n	i	s	t	s	u	o	i	r	a	v
n	i	i	r	e	c	e	i	p	t	d	j	m
t	o	l	n	o	i	t	f	a	n	e	v	i
n	u	i	s	t	e	r	a	d	r	c	d	n
o	s	e	r	i	o	u	s	r	e	l	e	o
i	p	c	o	n	t	i	h	o	l	a	c	i
h	a	s	u	e	s	k	i	n	g	r	i	s
s	r	t	t	c	r	s	o	t	g	e	s	i
u	e	e	e	r	a	r	n	i	u	t	i	v
c	o	s	a	m	a	j	y	p	m	t	o	i
p	r	o	v	i	s	i	o	n	s	s	n	d

Two Meanings

10. The list word 'rare' has more than one meaning. Write two sentences to show the difference.

(a) _____

_____

(b) _____

_____

Adding Endings

11. Complete the table.

(a)	dare	dares	dared	daring
(b)	seize			
(c)	spare			
(d)	declare			
(e)	explore			
(f)	console			
(g)	scale			
(h)	continue			

List Words	Test 1	Test 2	Test 3	Test 4	Test 5	T
wardrobe						
backward						
quadriplegic						
physical						
photograph						
paragraph						
absence						
silence						
commence						
committee						
independent						
injure						
disability						
emotion						
source						
refreshment						
athlete						
vehicle						
student						
racism						
earn						
skilful						

Look	Say	Cover	Write	Check

Difficult Words I Have Found	Test 1	Test 2	Test 3	T

Small Words

1. Write the list words which contain these small words.

    (a) rob _____

    (b) sour _____

    (c) fresh _____

    (d) dent _____

    (e) rag _____

    (f) ski _____

Word Worm

2. (a) Circle each list word you can find in the word worm.

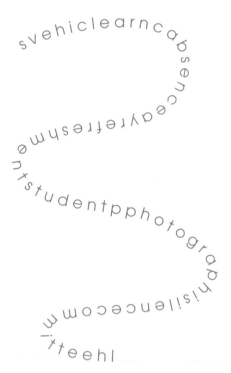

   (b) Write the list word you can make by unjumbling the remaining letters.

    _____

3. Use list words to solve the crossword.

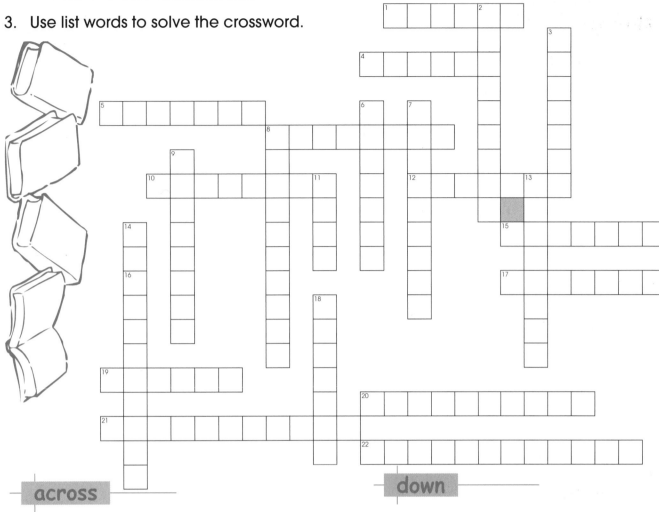

across

1. The beginning (of a river)
4. Offensive behaviour to members of another race
5. Showing skill
8. To do with the body
10. A cupboard for clothes
12. The state of being away
15. Feeling
17. A means of transport
19. To hurt or cause harm to
20. A physical or mental weakness or incapacity
21. Something that refreshes
22. Paralysed in the arms and legs

down

2. A group of people who deal with special business
3. A person trained in physical agility and strength
6. Freedom from noise
7. Part of a piece of writing
8. A picture taken by a camera
9. Opposite of forward
11. To receive money for work
13. Begin
14. Free to act by yourself
18. Pupil

Spelling Challenges

1. Write the list words using look, say, cover, write, check.
2. Write the list words in alphabetical order.
3. Write a paragraph containing 10 list words.
4. Sort the list words according to the number of syllables in each word.

Alphabetical Order

4. Put all the list and revision words with one syllable into alphabetical order. (9)

_____

_____

_____

_____

Missing Words

5. Use list words to complete the sentences.

(a) The crowd watched in _____ as the _____
    left the track before his race could _____.

(b) Inside the box, she found a black and white _____ of
    each _____ in the class and a _____
    written about each one.

(c) The _____ had been specially made for people with
    a _____, but you had to be very _____
    to drive it properly.

List
wardrobe
backward
quadriplegic
physical
photograph
paragraph
absence
silence
commence
committee
independent
injure
disability
emotion
source
refreshment
athlete
vehicle
student
racism
earn
skilful

Antonyms

6. Find a list or revision word with an opposite meaning.

(a) forward _____   (b) cease _____

(c) ability _____   (d) mental _____

(e) presence _____   (f) agree _____

Synonyms

7. Find a list or revision word with a similar meaning.

(a) cupboard _____   (b) organise _____

(c) start _____   (d) quiet _____

(e) picture _____   (f) pupil _____

Homonyms

8. Circle the correct words.

(a) The meat (sauce, source) dripped off his chin onto his shirt.

(b) The expedition travelled up the river to find its (sauce, source).

(c) James was able to (earn, urn) some extra pocket money by doing
    chores for his mother.

(d) The old (earn, urn) was decorated with a beautiful floral pattern.

Missing Letters

9. Write 'f', 'ph' or 'ff' to complete these words correctly.

(a) ____eet   (b) ____ysical (c) ____otograph (d) o____er

(e) ele____ant (f) terri____ic (g) ne____ew (h) geogra____y

Revision
arrange
freeze
pitch
contest
complain
truth
partner
turkey
forward
copper
hoof
argue
wonderful
anxious
knot
dictionary
area
imagine
yacht
guide
equal
senior

10. Find these list words in the word search.

wardrobe	injure
backward	vehicle
emotion	racism
physical	source
photograph	athlete
paragraph	absence
student	silence
skilful	commence
earn	committee

t	l	e	p	h	o	t	o	g	r	a	p	h
h	d	n	a	s	l	a	t	h	l	e	t	e
s	i	w	r	r	a	n	o	i	t	o	m	e
a	o	h	a	t	n	s	e	a	p	e	i	g
p	h	u	g	r	i	t	l	s	h	e	t	l
e	p	h	r	a	f	u	c	i	y	t	e	u
b	a	t	a	c	r	d	i	l	s	t	c	f
o	r	s	p	i	e	e	h	e	i	n	l
r	e	a	h	o	l	n	e	n	c	m	e	i
d	t	j	l	e	a	t	v	c	a	m	s	k
r	c	o	m	m	e	n	c	e	l	o	b	s
a	p	i	c	s	d	r	a	w	k	c	a	b
w	i	n	j	u	r	e	r	a	c	i	s	m

Better Words

11. Write a list word that is a synonym for the words in bold print.

(a) There was **no sound at all** as the party guests waited for the moment to yell 'surprise'. _____

(b) After many months of being ill, she finally felt **capable of doing things without anyone's help**. _____

(c) The falling rock didn't **cause harm to** me, because I moved out of the way just in time. _____

More Than One

12. Complete this table of plurals.

(a)	refreshment	
(b)	absence	
(c)	committee	
(d)	disability	
(e)	photograph	
(f)	turkey	
(g)	area	
(h)	vehicle	

Word Challenge

13. (a) Make at least 10 words from the word in the box. You can rearrange the letters.

refreshment

_____

_____

_____

_____

_____

_____

_____

(b) Circle the longest word.

List Words	Test 1	Test 2	Test 3	Test 4	Test 5	T
delicious						
unconscious						
sponge						
college						
military						
primary						
necessary						
secretary						
stationary						
vast						
choir						
volcano						
mosquito						
foreign						
variety						
veranda						
century						
scarce						
discipline						
knowledge						
appreciate						
intelligent						

Look	Say	Cover	Write	Check

Difficult Words I Have Found	Test 1	Test 2	Test 3	T

Word Hunt

1. Which list or revision words:

(a) are animals?

_____

_____

(b) can the suffix 'ed' be added to?

_____

_____

_____

(c) have a homonym?

_____

(d) begin with a silent letter?

_____

(e) could be made into a compound word by adding the word 'boy'?

_____

(f) are occupations?

_____

Word Challenge

2. (a) Make at least 10 words from the word in the box. You can rearrange the letters.

knowledge

_____

_____

_____

_____

_____

_____

(b) Circle the longest word.

3. Use list words to solve the crossword.

across

1. Huge
6. A group of singers
9. Having a high mental capacity
10. Rare
16. A cone shaped mountain that may erupt
17. The armed forces
18. Essential
20. Not moving
21. A type of sea animal
22. A covered outside area attached to a house

down

2. To value
3. A business assistant
4. That which is known
5. A small flying insect
7. Self-control
8. Belonging to another country
11. One hundred years
12. Opposite of conscious
13. The first or chief
14. Pleasant tasting
15. A mixed collection
19. A type of school

My Meanings

4. Write a definition for each of these words. Use a dictionary to check your answers.

(a) delicious _____

(b) choir _____

(c) mosquito _____

(d) necessary _____

Spelling Challenges

1. Write the list words using look, say, cover, write, check.
2. Sort the revision words according to the number of syllables.
3. Use a dictionary to write a definition for 10 list words.
4. Write the revision list in alphabetical order.

UNIT 16

All Mixed Up

5. Unjumble the list words.

(a) raecserty _____

(b) atilmyri _____

(c) elwonkegd _____

(d) acepaprite _____

(e) uciledios _____

(f) llocege _____

(g) onaclov _____

(h) gierofn _____

(i) dnareva _____

(j) aotastinyr _____

(k) yramirp _____

(l) riohc _____

(m) idcpniesli _____

(n) gnopse _____

Antonyms

6. Find a list or revision word with an opposite meaning.

(a) secondary _____

(b) conscious _____

(c) common _____

(d) unintelligent _____

(e) unnecessary _____

(f) senior _____

(g) moving _____

(h) northern _____

Synonyms

7. Find a list or revision word with a similar meaning.

(a) initial _____

(b) still _____

(c) huge _____

(d) alien _____

(e) rare _____

(f) truthful _____

(g) smart _____

(h) build _____

Sentences

8. Write sentences using the plural form of the following words.

(a) volcano _____

_____

(b) mosquito _____

_____

(c) veranda _____

_____

(d) century _____

List

delicious
unconscious
sponge
college
military
primary
necessary
secretary
stationary
vast
choir
volcano
mosquito
foreign
variety
veranda
century
scarce
discipline
knowledge
appreciate
intelligent

Revision

exchange
breeze
switch
construct
explain
honest
pardon
attend
author
customer
currant
avenue
canoe
accident
lettuce
guard
quality
marriage
neither
southern
type
junior

9. Find these list words in the word search.

d	i	s	c	i	p	l	i	n	e	a	s	t
e	s	i	o	y	r	a	s	s	e	c	e	n
c	u	y	a	p	p	r	e	c	i	a	t	e
r	o	c	e	n	t	u	r	y	t	t	m	g
a	i	o	n	a	c	l	o	v	s	y	o	i
c	c	o	l	l	e	g	e	e	a	r	s	l
s	i	m	h	r	p	y	g	r	v	a	q	l
f	l	r	g	c	t	r	n	a	a	t	u	e
v	e	g	d	e	l	w	o	n	k	i	i	t
e	d	r	i	m	m	t	p	d	r	l	t	n
f	o	r	e	i	g	n	s	a	f	i	o	i
v	a	s	y	r	a	m	i	r	p	m	d	a
v	r	s	t	y	r	a	t	e	r	c	e	s

delicious   mosquito

sponge   foreign

college   variety

military   veranda

primary   century

necessary   scarce

secretary   discipline

vast   knowledge

choir   appreciate

volcano   intelligent

Sound Search

10. In the word 'choir', the 'ch' says a 'k' sound. Find three other words where 'ch' says 'k' and put them in a sentence.

(a) _____

_____

(b) _____

_____

(c) _____

_____

Missing Letters

11. Write 'l' or 'll' to complete these words.

(a) mi____itary   (b) ho____iday

(c) qua____ity   (d) inte____igent

(e) co____ege   (f) ye____ow

(g) she____ter   (h) he____o

Homonyms

12. Circle the correct word.

(a) The lorry was (stationary, stationery) at the traffic light.

(b) It was time for the office manager to order some new (stationary, stationery) for the staff.

List Words	Test 1	Test 2	Test 3	Test 4	Test 5	T
dense						
immense						
gradual						
annual						
stereotype						
punctual						
serial						
principal						
expense						
prejudice						
attractive						
patient						
nutrition						
magazine						
medicine						
system						
difficult						
behaviour						
hymn						
president						
thorough						
consider						

 Look   Say   Cover   Write   Check

Difficult Words I Have Found	Test 1	Test 2	Test 3	T

Small Words

1. Find small words in these list words.

   (a) dense

   _____

   (b) patient

   _____

   (c) thorough

   _____

   (d) consider

   _____

   (e) annual

   _____

Word Worm

2. (a) Circle each list word you can find in the word worm.

econsidernaimmensexpenserialpitmedicinemtstereotypeprejudicemagazineyhm

   (b) Write the two list words you can make by unjumbling the remaining words.

   _____

   _____

3. Use list words to solve the crossword.

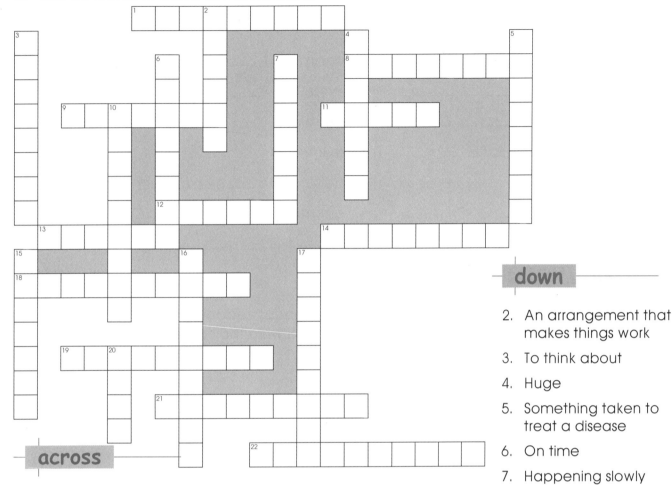

across

1. The head of a republic
8. A journal published regularly
9. Cost
11. Packed closely together
12. Happening yearly
13. A continuing story
14. Comprehensive
18. Pleasing to the eye
19. The way people act or conduct themselves
21. Food
22. A standardised idea

down

2. An arrangement that makes things work
3. To think about
4. Huge
5. Something taken to treat a disease
6. On time
7. Happening slowly and evenly
10. Chief person
15. Tolerant or persistent
16. Hard
17. An opinion based on little or no knowledge or experience
20. A religious song of praise

Two Meanings

4. The list word 'patient' has more than one meaning. Write two sentences to show the difference.

(a) _____

_____

_____

(b) _____

_____

_____

Spelling Challenges

1. Write the list words using look, say, cover, write, check.
2. Write each of the list words in a question.
3. Use a dictionary to write a definition for six list words.
4. Sort the list words according to the number of syllables.

All Mixed Up

5. Unjumble the list words.

(a) picnirpla _____

(b) izgamaen _____

(c) uorothhg _____

(d) laires _____

(e) dsnee _____

(f) esnmime _____

(g) nicideme _____

(h) evitcartta _____

(i) udrgaal _____

(j) ediserpnt _____

(k) itiruntno _____

(l) cnuptlau _____

(m) nmyh _____

(n) obhevaiur _____

Extend Yourself

6. The word 'annual' comes from the Latin word 'annus' meaning 'year'. Find three more words using this word base and write their meanings.

(a) _____

_____

(b) _____

_____

(c) _____

_____

Homonyms

7. Circle the correct word.

(a) The (principal/principle) of the company said the (principal/ principle) reason behind the decision to change the holiday roster was to suit as many staff as possible.

(b) The radio (cereal/serial) was sponsored by a breakfast (cereal/ serial) company.

(c) It was difficult for (him/hymn) to sing the (him/hymn) because it was too high for his voice.

(d) He pondered the (byte/bite) problem he was having with his computer as he took a (byte/bite) of toast.

(e) There was enough time for her to (practise/practice) passing with her Dad before netball (practise/practice) began.

List

dense
immense
gradual
annual
stereotype
punctual
serial
principal
expense
prejudice
attractive
patient
nutrition
magazine
medicine
system
difficult
behaviour
hymn
president
thorough
consider

Revision

phrase
queer
project
district
brain
practice
alarm
atom
metal
gardener
current
reduce
cement
bicycle
bother
guess
relative
museum
usual
double
byte
annoy

8. Find these list words in the word search.

dense

immense

gradual

annual

consider

punctual

serial

principal

expense

stereotype

patient

magazine

medicine

system

difficult

behaviour

hymn

president

thorough

s	e	u	t	r	u	o	i	v	a	h	e	b
t	n	n	l	s	y	s	t	e	m	p	l	r
e	i	s	a	n	l	a	u	d	a	r	g	t
r	c	s	u	d	r	n	n	u	g	l	n	t
e	i	u	n	n	e	c	i	e	a	l	h	l
o	d	a	n	z	d	n	z	s	z	a	g	a
t	e	l	a	f	i	e	s	n	i	u	u	p
y	m	p	r	e	s	i	d	e	n	t	o	i
p	i	z	e	n	n	e	e	m	e	c	r	c
e	m	t	e	n	o	u	r	m	t	n	o	n
p	u	p	m	a	c	h	v	i	s	u	h	i
x	x	y	r	t	n	e	i	t	a	p	t	r
e	h	l	d	i	f	f	i	c	u	l	t	p

Adding Beginnings

9. Write the correct prefix for these list or revision words.

(im) (un) (re) (mis) (bi)

(a) _____ usual

(b) _____ patient

(c) _____ behaviour

(d) _____ attractive

(e) _____ consider

(f) _____ annual

Alphabetical Order

10. Put all the list and revision words that end in 'e' into alphabetical order. (15)

_____

_____

_____

_____

Missing Letters

11. Write 'se' or 'ce' to complete these words.

(a) immen _____

(b) fen _____

(c) pen _____

(d) prin _____

(e) stan _____

(f) rin _____

(g) den _____

(h) boun _____

(i) expen _____

List Words	Test 1	Test 2	Test 3	Test 4	Test 5	T
nuclear						
politics						
fuel						
quarrel						
poultry						
villain						
migrant						
highway						
diamond						
traveller						
swollen						
vacant						
valve						
society						
occurred						
onion						
opinion						
champion						
religion						
language						
persuade						
sufficient						

Look **Say** **Cover** **Write** **Check**

Difficult Words I Have Found	Test 1	Test 2	Test 3	T

Word Meanings

1. Write the list word that matches each meaning.

   (a) not filled

   _____

   (b) a point of view on something

   _____

   (c) a set of beliefs

   _____

   (d) someone who is the best at what they do

   _____

   (e) to try to convince

   _____

Word Hunt

2. Which list words:

   (a) are compound words?

   _____

   (b) have more than three syllables?

   _____

   (c) are things people eat?

   _____

   _____

3. Use list words to solve the crossword.

across

1. Happened
3. Empty
6. Powered by atomic energy
7. A person who lives in a country that they did not originate from
8. One who travels
9. Farmyard fowls
12. A major road
13. Substance burnt in a combustion engine
14. Enlarged or puffed up
17. Enough
18. Viewpoint
19. The overall winner
20. The science of government
21. To make a person think your way

down

2. A precious stone
4. Argue
5. A bad person
10. The belief in a god
11. A device that allows water to flow in one direction only
15. A type of vegetable
16. Human speech
17. Individuals living as a community

Word Challenge

4. (a) Make at least 10 words from the word in the box. You can rearrange the letters.

persuade

_____

_____

_____

(b) Circle the longest word you found.

Spelling Challenges

1. Write the words using look, say, cover, write, check.

2. Write a nonsense paragraph containing fifteen list words.

3. Write the revision words in alphabetical order.

4. Sort the list words according to the number of vowels in each word.

Memory Master

List

nuclear
politics
fuel
quarrel
poultry
villain
migrant
highway
diamond
traveller
swollen
vacant
valve
society
occurred
onion
opinion
champion
religion
language
persuade
sufficient

5. (a) Cover the list words. Write three from memory.

_____   _____   _____

(b) For each word, write a question which has the word as its answer.

(i) _____

(ii) _____

(iii) _____

Antonyms

6. Find a list or revision word with an opposite meaning.

(a) insufficient _____   (b) host _____

(c) filled _____   (d) fact _____

(e) agreement _____   (f) destroy _____

Synonyms

7. Find a list or revision word with a similar meaning.

(a) argue _____   (b) happened _____

(c) barter _____   (d) starvation _____

(e) petrol _____   (f) make _____

(g) loyally _____   (h) enough _____

Better Words

8. Write a list word that is a synonym for the words in bold print.

(a) 'Those three pieces of chocolate cake should be **more than enough** for my afternoon tea,' she said greedily.

_____

(b) The chair next to me is not **occupied by anyone**.

_____

(c) When I sprained my ankle, it was **increased in size** for days.

_____

(d) We couldn't agree on which **group of people with a common goal** we all wanted to join.

_____

Revision

disgrace
indeed
product
stomach
jail
intend
bargain
atmosphere
technology
hunger
coconut
produce
caravan
biscuit
palm
guest
period
barrier
experience
whom
repair
faithfully

9. Find these list words in the word search.

n	o	i	p	m	a	h	c	u	q	e	a	l
i	n	t	r	a	y	r	t	l	u	o	p	a
n	o	i	n	i	p	o	v	o	a	r	y	n
m	i	g	r	r	v	m	e	n	r	a	a	g
r	d	n	o	m	a	i	d	i	r	e	w	u
d	s	i	n	u	c	g	a	o	e	l	h	a
e	c	a	n	g	a	r	u	n	l	c	g	g
r	i	l	e	d	n	a	s	a	i	u	i	e
r	t	l	l	e	t	n	r	y	a	n	h	v
u	i	i	l	f	u	t	e	a	e	r	p	l
c	l	v	o	t	u	u	p	p	r	r	i	a
c	o	h	w	y	t	e	i	c	o	s	p	v
o	p	u	s	e	r	e	l	i	g	i	o	n

nuclear

champion

swollen

fuel

language

valve

poultry

villain

migrant

highway

diamond

society

religion

vacant

quarrel

persuade

politics

occurred

onion

opinion

Missing Words

10. Use list words to complete the sentences.

(a) In my _____, we should have _____

_____ in the tank to reach our destination.

(b) They had a furious _____ about who owned the

_____.

(c) The newly arrived _____ did not understand a word of the

_____ of her new country.

Adding Endings

11. Add these suffixes to as many of these list and revision words as possible.

ed	ing	ly	y	sion

(a) intend   intended, intending

(b) quarrel   _____

(c) persuade   _____

(d) sufficient   _____

(e) experience   _____

(f) hunger   _____

Interesting Words from my Writing

Date	Word	Date	Word	Date	Word

Interesting Words from my Writing

Date	Word	Date	Word	Date	Word

My Dictionary Words: Aa to Ii

Aa

Bb

Cc

Dd

Ee

Ff

Gg

Hh

Ii

Jj

Kk

Ll

Mm

Nn

Oo

Pp

Qq

Rr

My Dictionary Words: **S** *s* to **Z** z

Ss

Tt

Uu

Vv

Ww

Xx

Yy

Zz